Parent/Teachers: Give children brief directions on how to do each job. Work along with the child when necessary. Allow the child to work independently when ready. Discuss the jobs after each page is completed. For more suggestions, please read Book 10.

Expand on Bob's Jobs by providing inexpensive paper, crayons, pencils, and pens for child to create original drawings and words. Take dictation from the child. Stories can be about Bob Books characters or from children's imagination. Have short work times and have fun with the jobs!

by Bobby Lynn Maslen   pictures by John R. Maslen

Scholastic Inc.

New York • Toronto • London • Auckland • Sydney • Mexico City • New Delhi • Hong Kong

Color the pictures in this book

**Ask for Bob Books at your local bookstore, visit www.bobbooks.com,
or call: 1-800-733-5572.**

ISBN 0-439-17568-2

12 11 10 9 8 7 6 5   1 2 3 4 5/0
Printed in the U.S.A.   10

Book 1

Floppy Mop

Circle the correct word.

Mop was a big

dag

dig

dog

Mop was Tom's

pad

pat

pal

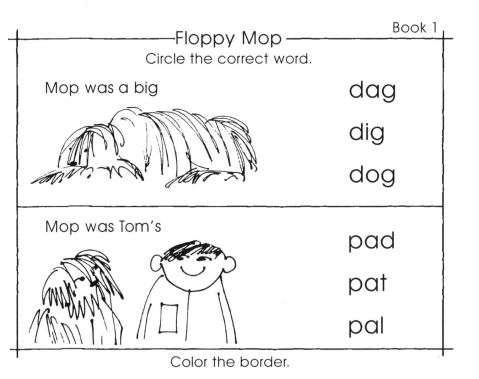

Color the border.

Circle the correct word.

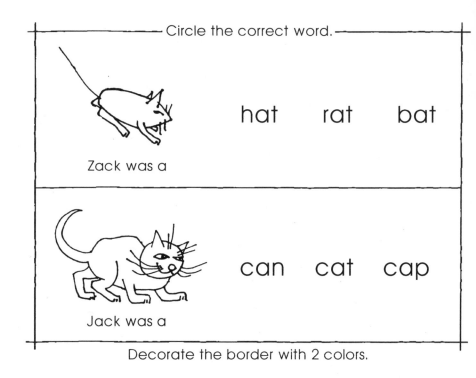

hat   rat   bat

Zack was a

can   cat   cap

Jack was a

Decorate the border with 2 colors.

Mop was Tom's pal.

Color Tom and Mop.

Give Mop some more bones.

Book 2

Lolly-Pops

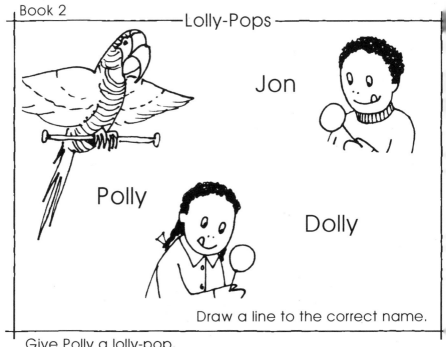

Jon

Polly

Dolly

Draw a line to the correct name.

Give Polly a lolly-pop.

Color Polly. Color Dolly. Color Jon.

Jon

Dolly

Polly

Where did they go?
To the

_____ _____ _____

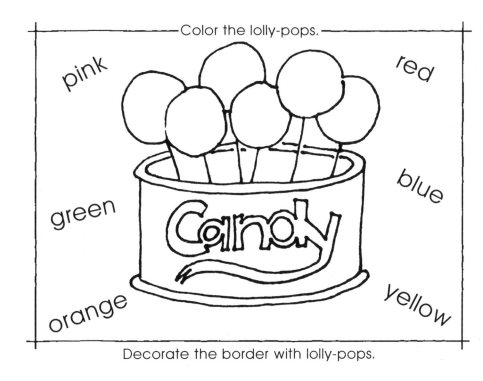

Color the lolly-pops.

pink

red

blue

green

Candy

orange

yellow

Decorate the border with lolly-pops.

Frogs

Color the frogs.

Follow the dots. Begin at •

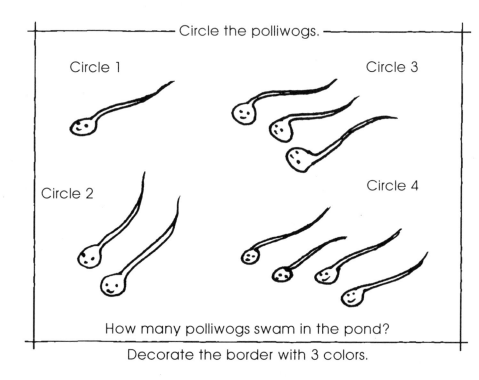

Circle the polliwogs.

Circle 1

Circle 3

Circle 2

Circle 4

How many polliwogs swam in the pond?

Decorate the border with 3 colors.

Color the border.

dive

jump

jump

dive

swim   hide

swim

hide

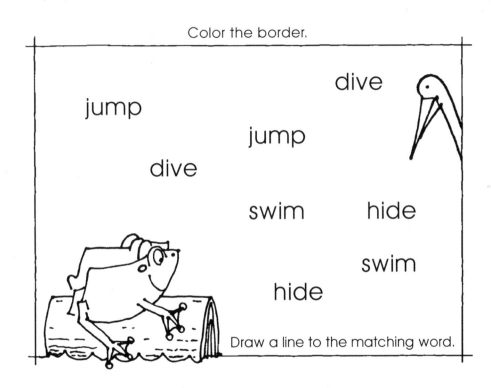

Draw a line to the matching word.

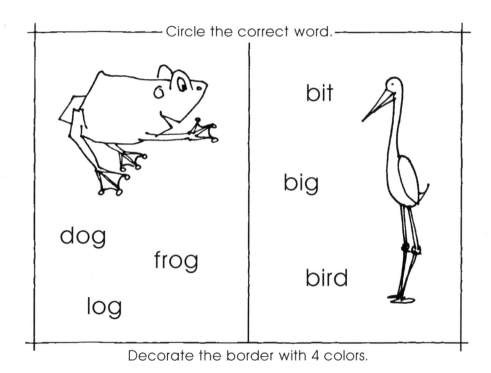

Circle the correct word.

dog

frog

log

bit

big

bird

Decorate the border with 4 colors.

Book 4

The Red Car

Draw a **girl** in the car. Draw a **boy** in the car.

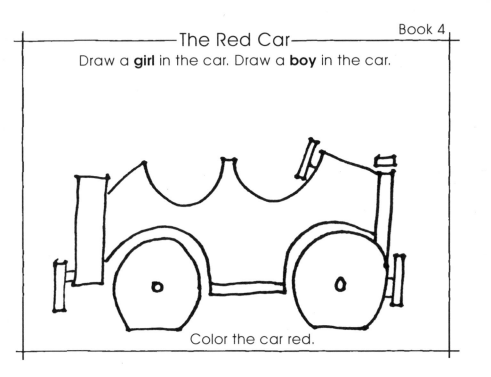

Color the car red.

Decorate the border.

_____ ar   c

_____ _____ ar   st

_____ _____ art   st

_____ _____ art   sm

Write the correct letter on the line.
Read the words.

Draw a line to the correct word.

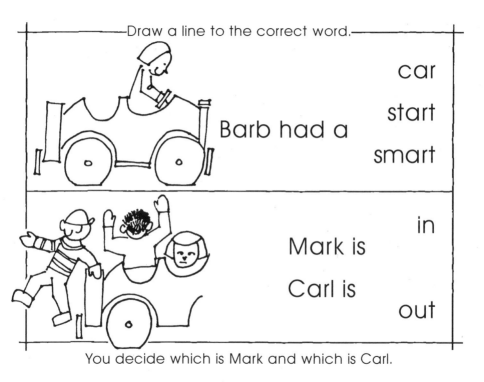

Barb had a

car

start

smart

Mark is

Carl is

in

out

You decide which is Mark and which is Carl.